GW00392953

MEMORIES RECORDED BY

_____

FOR

_____

GRANDMOTHER REMEMBERS

Memories to share with your grandchildren

Illustrations by Lucy Su

◆ ◆ ◆

Text by Jean Kellaway

BLITZ EDITIONS

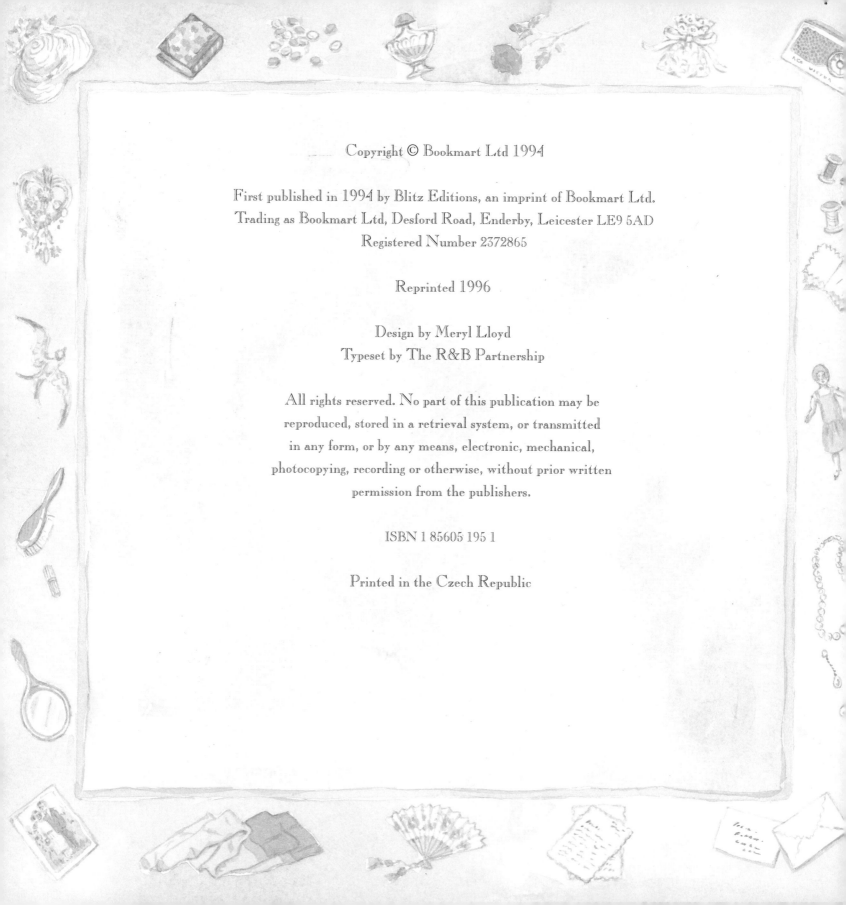

CONTENTS

◇ ◇ ◇

FAMILY TREE

✧ ✧ ✧

The strands of your heritage spread back through the ages. Here is a lasting record of your immediate ancestors which you will one day pass on to your own children.

✧ Photographs of great grandparents ✧

Grandfather's father

_____

Grandfather's mother

_____

Grandmother's father

_____

Grandmother's mother

_____

Mother's father

_____

Mother's mother

_____

Mother

_____

Mother's brothers and sisters

_____

_____

Grandfather's father

_____

Grandfather's mother

_____

Grandmother's father

_____

Grandmother's mother

_____

Father's father

_____

Father's mother

_____

Father

_____

Father's brothers and sisters

_____

_____

Children

_____

_____

MY EARLY YEARS

✦ ✧ ✦

Long ago, I was a helpless baby, a tottering toddler and an enquiring
child – just like you. Here are some of my earliest memories
of those far-off days.

I was born on

_____

I weighed

_____

The place was

_____

My mother's full name

_____

My father's full name

_____

Their jobs

_____

My brothers and sisters

_____

_____

We lived at

_____

My favourite toys were

_____

✧ Photographs and souvenirs ✧

MY SCHOOLDAYS

◇ ✦ ◇

Satchels and sweets, homework and headmasters, making friends
and having fun; school days are made of this. Mostly happy, occasionally tearful,
the years fall away when I recall these important first days in my life.

We lived at

_____

My first school was

_____

My favourite teacher was

_____

My best friends were

_____

My favourite subject was

_____

I wore

_____

My secondary school was

_____

My favourite teacher was

_____

My best friends were

_____

My favourite subject was

_____

I wore

_____

On sportsdays I

_____

In the playground I

_____

For lunch I ate

_____

School achievements

_____

_____

The clubs I belonged to included

_____

_____

The best moment of school was

_____

The worst moment of school was

_____

◇ Photographs and souvenirs ◇

MY TEENAGE YEARS

◇ ◇ ◇

Embarking on life, I was filled with great expectations.
I had my hopes and dreams, just like every other youngster. Some became
reality, others fell by the wayside as the years rolled by. Now I'd like
to share those precious inner thoughts with you.

I lived at

My closest friends were

My dreams

The fashions were

My fears

My favourite singer was

At weekends and in the evenings I

My first job was

Things I considered most
important were

Things I considered least
important were

❖ Photographs and souvenirs ❖

HOW I MET YOUR GRANDFATHER

◆ ◇ ◆

Although I'd known some good times, your grandfather brought a
vital zest and zing to my life. Even the air I breathed seemed
sweeter after we met. That magic time is recalled here.

My age

_____

His age

_____

We met at

_____

He was wearing

_____

I was wearing

_____

His first words were

_____

My first words were

_____

My first impression was

_____

His first impression was

_____

◇ Photographs and souvenirs ◇

YOUR GRANDFATHER AS A CHILD

◇ ◇ ◇

Of course, your grandfather has his own tale to tell. He had a different life to mine which shaped his views on the ways of the world. This is how his story starts.

Your grandfather's full name

_____

His mother's full name

_____

His father's full name

_____

Their jobs

_____

_____

Your grandfather lived at

_____

His first school was

_____

His secondary school was

_____

His best subjects were

_____

_____

His worst subjects were

His dreams were

_____

Brothers and sisters

His fears were

_____

◇ Photographs and souvenirs ◇

GRANDFATHER AS A YOUNG MAN

◇ ◇ ◇

By the time I met your grandfather he already had his own opinions
and ideas. He was a fine young man filled with enthusiasm and energy,
ready to take on the world. Here is a glimpse of his youth.

He lived at

_____

His job was

_____

His best friends were

_____

His first car was

_____

He disliked

_____

He loved

_____

At the weekends and in the
evenings he

_____

His hobbies were

_____

His ambition was

_____

Previous girlfriends included

_____

Things he considered most
important were

_____

_____

_____

Things he considered least
important were

_____

_____

_____

◈ Photographs ◈

OUR COURTSHIP

◇ ◇ ◇

Falling in love means a thousand things. A clasped hand, a slow
dance, a certain smile; all can say in that special way: 'I love you'.
Like the spring flowers, our love grew and blossomed just as your
own romance surely will one day.

Our first date

_____

Our most memorable date

_____

Our favourite meal

_____

Pet names we had for each other were

_____

_____

He proposed

_____

_____

His words were

_____

My response was

_____

Special love tokens exchanged included

_____

What my parents thought

_____

_____

What his parents thought

_____

_____

◇ Photographs and souvenirs ◇

◇ 19 ◇

OUR WEDDING

✦ ✦ ✦

A wedding day brims over with mixed emotions. The elation and
rapture go hand in hand with tension and nerves. It does not always
turn out just as you planned. But however it unfolds, it is always
moving and memorable.

It took place on

_____

The venue was

_____

I wore

_____

He wore

_____

My attendants included

_____

They wore

_____

The best man was

_____

I was given away by

_____

Ushers were

_____

My flowers were

_____

The reception was held at

_____

Guests included

_____

Among the gifts were

Music that reminds me of the day

⬦ Photographs and souvenirs ⬦

OUR HONEYMOON

✦ ✦ ✦

After the commotion of the wedding, it is time to retreat for a few
days or weeks of tranquility, to reflect on the big day. For some, it is
a luxurious hotel in a far-flung resort. For others, a few days at
home, sweet home. No matter where, it marks the start of life's
journey together instead of being alone.

We spent our wedding night at

_____

_____

Our honeymoon destination was

_____

_____

We stayed at

_____

_____

_____

Our most memorable moment was

_____

_____

_____

My precious mementoes of
that time are

_____

_____

_____

_____

◇ Photographs and souvenirs ◇

I USED TO...

◇ ◆ ◇

Here's your chance to sneak a glance at how I was when I was
younger. My life has changed in so many ways ~ I'm older and wiser
now ~ yet parts of me will always remain the same.

My favourite clothes

_____

Vices

_____

My favourite shoes

_____

Virtues

_____

How I felt about children

_____

_____

How I spent my weekdays

_____

_____

How I felt about politics

_____

_____

How I spent my weekends

_____

_____

My pastimes

_____

_____

My biggest worries were

_____

_____

The season I loved best was

_____

My favourite flowers were

_____

_____

Headlines I remember from
the time include

_____

_____

_____

◇ Photographs ◇

GRANDFATHER USED TO...

◇ ◇ ◇

It's hard to believe the man I married has now earned the title
'grandad'. Apart from a few smile lines and a different hairstyle, to
me he seems the same young man who walked me down the aisle.

His favourite clothes

_____

His favourite shoes

_____

His hobbies

_____

His favourite sport

_____

His top entertainer

_____

His favourite music

_____

_____

His vices

_____

His virtues

_____

We lived at

_____

He worked as

_____

Inventions that changed our
lives include

_____

_____

_____

✧ Photographs and souvenirs ✧

OUR CHILDREN

✧ ✧ ✧

We cherished and nurtured your parent once, just as your parents
are now doing for you. Hard to believe the able adult on whom you
depend was once our babe in arms, so fragile and helpless. These are
poignant memories of that time.

Your parent was born on

_____

Weighing

_____

Place

_____

Full name

_____

Colour of hair at birth

_____

My first thoughts

_____

Grandfather's first thoughts

_____

_____

Brother and sisters

_____

_____

Birth dates and places

_____

_____

Your parent's first word

_____

Favourite toys

_____

Childhood

_____

_____

Teenage years

_____

_____

Mischief and mayhem

_____

_____

Interests

_____

_____

Magic moments

_____

_____

Favourite music

_____

_____

✧ Photographs and souvenirs ✧

◆ More photographs and souvenirs ◆

♦ More photographs and souvenirs ♦

FAMILY HOLIDAYS

✧ ✧ ✧

The thrill of golden breaks away from the rigours of routine never
fades. The weather may have been hazy but my memories of the
frolics, fun and freedom of those halcyon days remain pin sharp.
After all, what better souvenir could I bring home?

Our favourite holiday destination was

_____

We travelled there by

_____

We liked it there because

_____

Other holidays we had included

_____

_____

_____

Our children's reactions to sea
and sand were

_____

_____

Our worst moment on holiday was

_____

_____

Our best moment on holiday was

_____

_____

Our first trip abroad was

_____

We travelled there by

_____

What we liked best about
being abroad was

_____

_____

What we liked least about
being abroad was

_____

_____

Our best holiday ever was

_____

⋄ Photographs and souvenirs ⋄

◇ More photographs and souvenirs ◇

◇ More photographs and souvenirs ◇

FAMILY WEDDINGS

◇ ◇ ◇

One minute we had tiny children. The next, they were preparing to
take vows at the altar just as we had done ourselves years before.
The years had galloped past but that did not diminish the joy we
knew as we witnessed our youngsters seal their happiness.

Your mother and father met

_____

They married on

_____

The venue was

_____

Your mother wore

_____

Your father wore

_____

Best man was

_____

Bridesmaids were

_____

_____

The reception was held at

_____

Guests included

_____

_____

_____

_____

The most memorable moments
of the day were

_____

_____

_____

For their honeymoon they went

_____

Other weddings in our family

_____

_____

_____

◇ Photographs and souvenirs ◇

◇ More photographs and souvenirs ◇

✧ More photographs and souvenirs ✧

OUR GRANDCHILDREN

✦ ✦ ✦

Our hearts soared when we knew we were to be grandparents.
We went through the anxieties and expectations of the pregnancies
every bit as much as new mums. And it was a proud and exhilarating
moment when we welcomed new members to the family.

You were born on

_____

_____

We first met you

_____

_____

My initial thoughts were

_____

_____

Grandfather's initial thoughts were

_____

_____

Our gift to you was

_____

_____

Other grandchildren

_____

_____

_____

Our hopes and dreams for your future

_____

_____

_____

◇ Photographs and souvenirs ◇

FAMILY BIRTHDAYS

✧ ✧ ✧

Each passing year, the celebrations we have to honour
family birthdays seem to be filled with ever more love and tenderness.
Little in life compares with the delight in seeing the family
together for these festivities.

◇ Photographs and souvenirs ◇

SPECIAL OCCASIONS

✧ ✦ ✧

Christmas, Easter, anniversaries, sports days and prize givings – they
would not be the same without all the generations of our family
uniting to mark them in our own special way.

✧ Photographs and souvenirs ✧

CHERISHED MEMORIES

❖ ❖ ❖

Nothing has enriched my life more than watching my family
flourish. As we continue through life together, I can't help but wonder
at the enchantment and gladness that you have all given me.

✧ Photographs and souvenirs ✧

✧ 47 ✧

FAMILY RECIPES

◇ ◆ ◇

Cookery may not interest you yet, But when you one day become
nostalgic for the smells and tastes of your childhood, a favourite family
recipe is the best way to conjure up those sweet aromas –
and speed you back in time.

_____   _____

_____   _____

_____   _____

_____   _____

_____   _____

_____   _____

_____   _____

_____   _____

_____   _____

_____   _____

◇ Recipes ◇